Holiday Color Combinations

When we think about Christmas, we think of red and green! But there are lots of color combinations that work well with the holidays, creating contrast, soothing harmony, dramatic impact, or joyful exuberance. Let's look at some possible combinations.

Red and Green: This is the most traditional of the holiday combinations and immediately telegraphs Christmas.

Red and Gold: Use metallics to add sparkle that brings to mind golden decorations and glittering lights.

Red, Orange, Pink, Green, Chartreuse, and Turquoise: Combinations that add in these tertiary colors have a more contemporary feel and fresh modern edge. Pink and turquoise are great for smaller accent colors.

Neutral Tones and Pastels: White and cream of snow and sugar, brown and gray from nature's birch trees and pinecones—these soft natural tones combine nicely with muted gold and silver and a pop of red berries. Pastel colors add a delicate tone.

Black, White, and Gray: Feeling soft and quiet? Shades of gray with soft pastels are soothing and sweet. Bold black and white create a mor intense contrast and drama a look great with some pops o bright colors like the classic and green.

Color Stories

These two samples use either a warm or a cool palette for most of the composition. The red image is in warm, romantic tones of red, pink, orange, and yellow. In the blue image, I used shades of orange, pink, and yellow as accents—they are opposites on the color wheel from the cool shades, and I thought they added a good pop of color and interest so the piece is not too monochromatic.

These two samples use more neutrals, pastels, and black and white to create unique feels. I wanted to keep the background light on the first image. I played more with shading—which adds a lot of depth—and adding decorative dots to the bars and angel wings. In the black and white composition, there is a more dramatic feel created from the high contrast. I went back in with a white pencil (or white corrective ink pen) to add more lines for texture in the background bars.

Color Moods

We create a mood in a piece by the colors we choose to work with. It's not that there is a right or wrong answer, just that there are many ways to approach the coloring of an image. You can create a lot of contrast, little contrast, single-color stories, vibrant rich colors, or soothing pastels. The angels below are colored in two different ways. I think of the right angel as more snowy, soft, and delicate, while the left angel is joyful, bright, and bold. Experiment with colors to see what combinations feel the best to you in your chosen illustration!

Colored pencils (Prismacolor).
Color by Robin Pickens.

Markers (Tombow), colored pencils
(Prismacolor). Color by Robin Pickens.

Markers (Tombow), colored pencils
(Prismacolor). Color by Robin Pickens.

I'm Dreaming of a White Christmas

Markers (Tombow), colored pencils
(Prismacolor). Color by Robin Pickens.

Gifts of time and love are surely the basic ingredients of a truly merry Christmas.

—Peg Bracken

_____
_____
_____
_____
_____
_____
_____
_____
_____
_____
_____

Three Wise Men

And the angel said to them, "Fear not, for behold, I bring you good news of great joy that will be for all the people. For unto you is born this day in the city of David a Savior, who is Christ the Lord."

—Luke 2:10-11

Uplift Angel

5 GOLDEN RINGS

Christmas is a day of meaning and traditions,
a special day spent in the warm circle
of family and friends.

—Margaret Thatcher

Five Golden Rings

It's beginning to look a lot like Christmas;
Soon the bells will start,
And the thing that will make them ring
Is the carol that you sing
Right within your heart.

—Meredith Wilson, *It's Beginning to Look a Lot Like Christmas*

Bell

The best of all gifts around any Christmas tree: the presence of a happy family all wrapped up in each other.

—Burton Hillis

_____
_____
_____
_____
_____
_____
_____
_____
_____
_____

Joyous Bird

When they saw the star, they rejoiced exceedingly with great joy.

—Matthew 2:10

_____

Bethlehem Star

It is Christmas in the heart that
puts Christmas in the air.

—W. T. Ellis

_____

_____

_____

_____

_____

_____

_____

_____

_____

_____

Bird on Bow

Hark! The Herald Angels sing
Glory to the newborn king!

—**Charles Wesley,** *Hark! The Herald Angels Sing*

Candle Angel

Christmas, my child, is love in action.
Every time we love, every time
we give, it's Christmas.

—Dale Evans

Chickadees

Christmas! 'Tis the season for kindling
the fire of hospitality in the hall,
the genial fire of charity in the heart.

—Washington Irving

Two Wreaths

I will honor Christmas in my heart,
and try to keep it all the year.

—Charles Dickens, *A Christmas Carol*

Praying Angel

For to us a child is born, to us a son is given....
And he will be called Wonderful Counselor,
Mighty God, Everlasting Father,
Prince of Peace.

—Isaiah 9:6

Holy Family

Love came down at Christmas;
Love all lovely, love divine;
Love was born at Christmas,
Stars and angels gave the sign.

—Christina Rossetti, *Love Came Down at Christmas*

Horn Angel

I heard the bells on Christmas Day
Their old, familiar carols play,
And wild and sweet
The words repeat
Of peace on earth,
good-will to men!

—Henry Wadsworth Longfellow, *Christmas Bells*

Jingle Bells

Christmas waves a magic wand over this world, and behold, everything is softer and more beautiful.

—Norman Vincent Peale

I'm Dreaming of a White Christmas

May Christmas lend a special charm
To all you chance to do.
And may the season light your way
To hopes and dreams anew.

—**Garnett Ann Schultz,** *My Christmas Wish*

Mittens

Noel

BORN
is the
KING of
ISRAEL

Christmas is not a time or a season
but a state of mind. To cherish peace and
good will, to be plenteous in mercy, is to
have the real spirit of Christmas.

—Calvin Coolidge

Noel

Christmas is a box of tree ornaments
that have become part of the family.

—Charles M. Schulz

Ornaments

The joy of brightening other lives,
bearing each others' burdens, easing
others' loads, and supplanting empty hearts
and lives with generous gifts becomes
for us the magic of Christmas.

—W.C. Jones

_____
_____
_____
_____
_____
_____
_____
_____
_____

Joy Banner

Christmas day is a day of joy and charity.
May God make you very rich in both.

—Phillips Brooks

_____
_____
_____
_____
_____
_____
_____
_____
_____
_____
_____

The flow of blessings in our life is directly related to our passing blessings along to someone else.

—Thomas Kinkade

Peace and Noel

Christmas is a season not only of rejoicing but of reflection.

—Winston Churchill

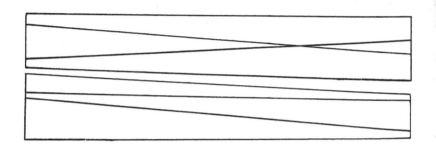

Bless us Lord, this Christmas,
with a quietness of mind;
Teach us to be patient
and always to be kind.

—Helen Steiner Rice

Shepherd Boy

The most exquisite Christmas ornaments
are made with little hands, full hearts,
glitter and glue.

—Deborah Whipp

Ornament

We saw His star when it rose and
have come to worship Him.

—Matthew 2:2

Star and Greens

UPLIFT OUR HEARTS

Christmas celebrates the awesome and amazing fact that God is grander, wiser, and more mysterious than we could have ever imagined.

—Dan Schaeffer

Uplift Our Hearts

> At Christmas play and make good cheer,
> for Christmas comes but once a year.
>
> —Thomas Tusser

Christmas Goose